LATIN
Playalong *for* Trumpet

GW00671077

WISE PUBLICATIONS
London/New York/Paris/Sydney/Copenhagen/Madrid/Tokyo

Exclusive Distributors:
Music Sales Limited
8/9 Frith Street, London W1D 3JB, England.
Music Sales Pty Limited
120 Rothschild Avenue, Rosebery, NSW 2018, Australia.

Order No. AM967758
ISBN 0-7119-8542-1
This book © Copyright 2001 by Wise Publications.

Compiled by Nick Crispin.
Music arranged by Jack Long.
Music processed by Enigma Music Production Services.
Cover photography by George Taylor.
Printed in the United Kingdom by Page Bros., Norwich, Norfolk.

CD produced by Music By Design.
Instrumental solos by Tony Fisher.
Engineered by Kester Sims.

Your Guarantee of Quality:
As publishers, we strive to produce every book to
the highest commercial standards.
The music has been freshly engraved and the book has been
carefully designed to minimise awkward page turns and
to make playing from it a real pleasure.
Particular care has been given to specifying acid-free, neutral-sized
paper made from pulps which have not been elemental chlorine bleached.
This pulp is from farmed sustainable forests and was
produced with special regard for the environment.
Throughout, the printing and binding have been planned to
ensure a sturdy, attractive publication which should give years of enjoyment.
If your copy fails to meet our high standards,
please inform us and we will gladly replace it.

Music Sales' complete catalogue describes thousands of
titles and is available in full colour sections by subject,
direct from Music Sales Limited.
Please state your areas of interest and send a
cheque/postal order for £1.50 for postage to:
Music Sales Limited, Newmarket Road, Bury St. Edmunds, Suffolk IP33 3YB.

www.musicsales.com

Trumpet Fingering Chart

MOUTHPIECE

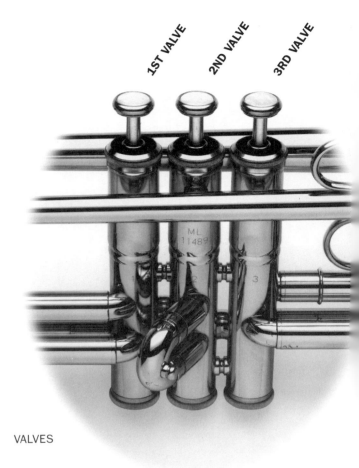

1ST VALVE 2ND VALVE 3RD VALVE

VALVES

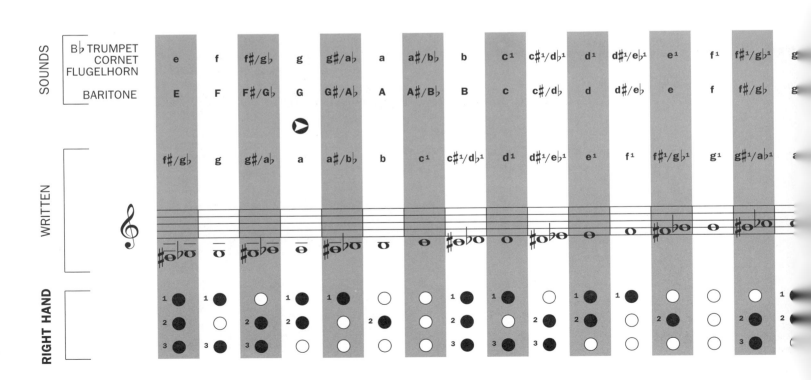

	SOUNDS																
B♭ TRUMPET CORNET FLUGELHORN	e	f	f♯/g♭	g	g♯/a♭	a	a♯/b♭	b	c¹	c♯¹/d♭¹	d¹	d♯¹/e♭¹	e¹	f¹	f♯¹/g♭¹	g
BARITONE	E	F	F♯/G♭	G	G♯/A♭	A	A♯/B♭	B	c	c♯/d♭	d	d♯/e♭	e	f	f♯/g♭	g

WRITTEN

f♯/g♭ · g · g♯/a♭ · a · a♯/b♭ · b · c¹ · c♯¹/d♭¹ · d¹ · d♯¹/e♭¹ · e¹ · f¹ · f♯¹/g♭¹ · g¹ · g♯¹/a♭¹ · a

RIGHT HAND

Indicates the lower limit of the best playing range

Transposition

The Bb trumpet, cornet and flugelhorn
sound a major second below the written pitch.
Rule: **Written C sounds Bb**

Written:    Sounds: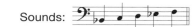

The baritone sounds a major ninth below
the written pitch. Rule: **Written C sounds Bb**

Written:    Sounds:

Pitch System

The letter names which appear at the top of the
fingering chart indicate the relative octave as well as
the name of each pitch, as shown below.

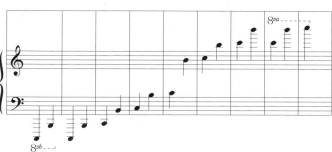

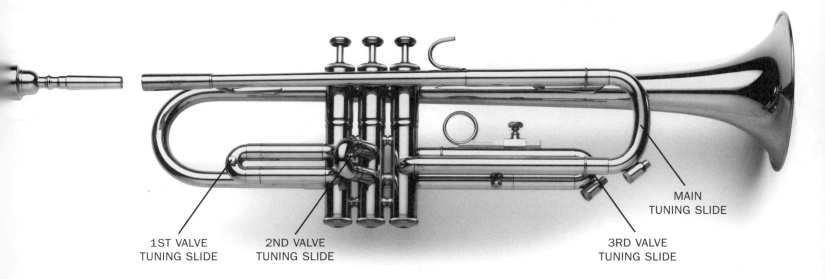

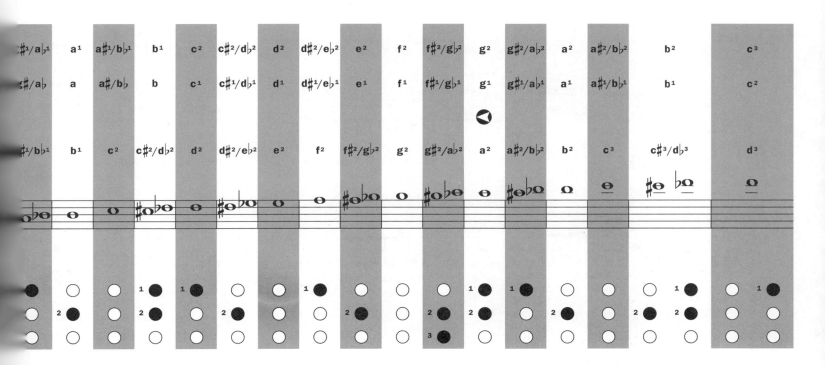

◄ Indicates the upper limit of the best playing range

Dos Gardenias

Words & Music by Isolina Carrillo

Besame Mucho

Words & Music by Consuelo Velazquez

The Girl From Ipanema
(Garota De Ipanema)

Original Words by Vinicius De Moraes
Music by Antonio Carlos Jobim
English Words by Norman Gimbel

Guantanamera

Words Adapted by Julian Orbon from a poem by José Marti
Music Adaptation by Pete Seeger & Julian Orbon

p poco a poco cresc.

mp

mf

dim.

mp

rit.

La Bamba

Traditional
Adapted & Arranged by Ritchie Valens

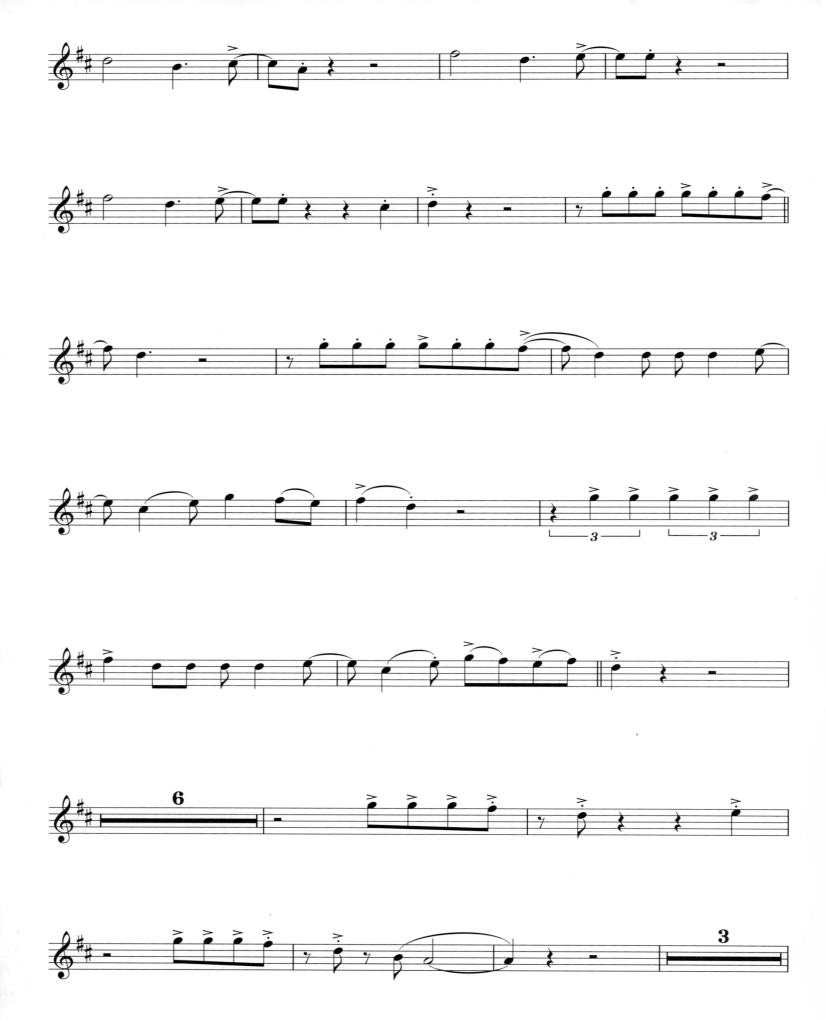

Lambada

Words & Music by Ulises Hermosa, Gonzales Hermosa, Alberto Maravi, Marcia Ferreira & Jose Ari
Music by Ulises Hermosa & Gonzales Hermosa

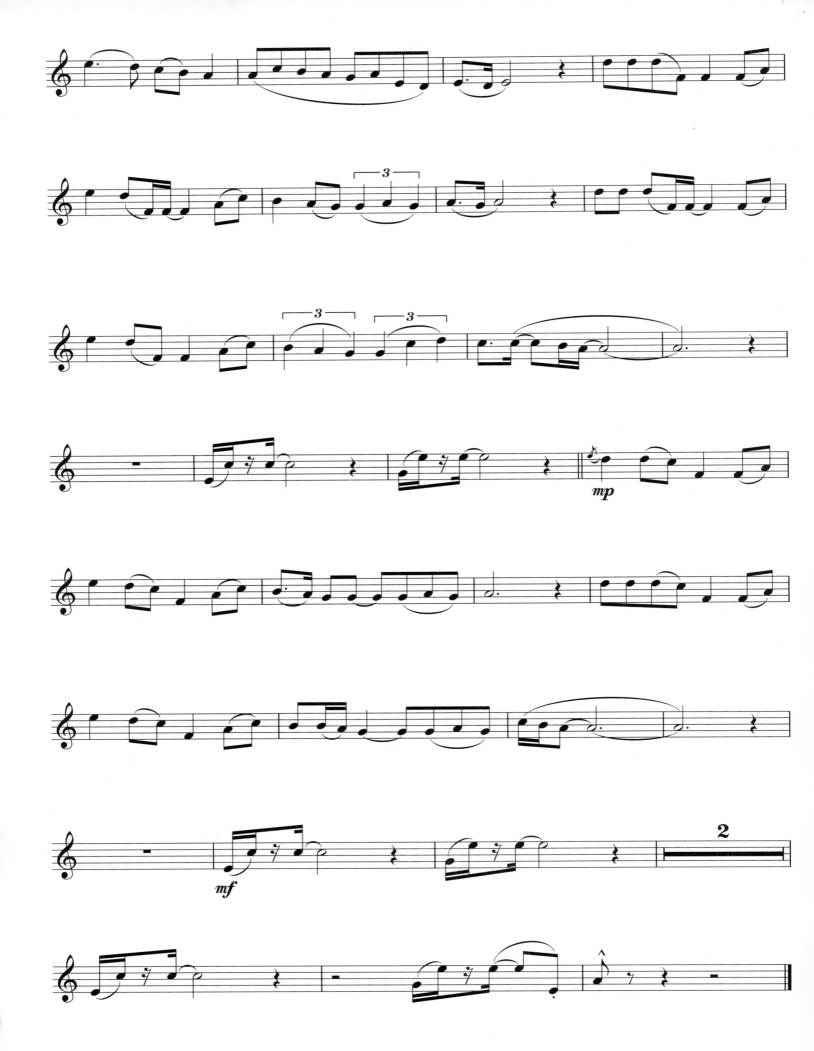

Mas Que Nada

Words & Music by Jorge Ben

Perhaps, Perhaps, Perhaps
(Quizas, Quizas, Quizas)

Original Words & Music by Osvaldo Farres
English Words by Joe Davis

Sway (Quien Sera)

Original Words & Music by Pablo Beltran Ruiz
English Words by Normal Gimbel

Oye Como Va

Words & Music by Tito Puente

Medium tempo

(fall)